JACK COOGINS

By Space Ship to the Moon

BY SPACE SHIP TO THE MOON

By JACK COGGINS and FLETCHER PRATT

RANDOM HOUSE · NEW YORK

V 3569   Random House   F P   7-25-58

Introduction

Space travel was first talked of by the mathematicians and theoretical scientists. They said that space travel would become possible if the engineers were able to do this thing and that thing.

Now the engineers are talking about space travel. They are confident that they can do the things that need to be done to bring it about. They don't say that they can do it today or tomorrow; nor do they say that it will be easy. But they do say that, if given some time (say between twelve and twenty years) and the necessary money (a few billion dollars, or about as much as was given to the Atomic Energy program) they can build a station in space and a moon ship, too.

The doctors are also talking about space travel these days. In fact, they are talking about it much earlier than they had expected they would be. The doctors had thought that they would not be called upon to contribute their specialized knowledge until the engineers had progressed much further than they have at this moment. But then it turned out that the pilots of high-flying aircraft had, in a way, reached "space."

It must be remembered that the high-flying airplanes of today are still just airplanes and not space ships; but, since so little air is left at a height of 65,000 feet, a special breathing apparatus had to be devised for the pilots. As a result, many of the problems which were believed to be applicable only to spaceship pilots of the future turned out to apply to some airplane pilots of today. So, strangely enough, some of these problems may be solved by the doctors long before the engineers are ready with space ships.

But whenever people talk about space travel they usually speak about the "trip to the moon."

They do this even though they know very well that the moon is not a comfortable place. It is an interesting place, of course, and it may have a certain usefulness, but it cannot be called pleasant even by the dyed-in-the-wool space-travel enthusiast.

Nevertheless, the moon is nearer to us than any other body in the universe. And it is this fact which first put the idea of space travel into Man's head. The other planets, including Mars and Venus, are so far away that even at their brightest they appear only as luminous points in the sky. But the moon was recognized as a massive body even before the telescope was invented.

Since the moon is so obviously another world in the sky, it was at first suspected, and later on proved, that the other planets are worlds too. And once the idea of the existence of other worlds becomes a certainty, the imagination seizes on the possibility of going to those worlds.

So it was the moon that started the whole idea of space travel. And, worth while or not, it will be the first heavenly body to be reached by Man.

—WILLY LEY

Who Pays For It?

Do you want to go exploring through space? We can start preparing for the trip tomorrow morning, provided someone will put up the money. Because the moon is nearer to the earth than any other body in the sky, it would be a wise choice for a first stopping place.

The trip is fun to think about and talk about, and we can solve most of the problems, at least on paper. But the really big question is: Who's going to pay for it? At the very least it would cost a couple of billion dollars.

There is nobody on earth rich enough to pay for a rocket that would go to the moon. The big business corporations might possibly find the money, but they would want to see some way of getting it back. At pres-

ent, it is believed that many valuable minerals are to be found on the moon, but nobody knows for sure. It is not very likely that the big corporations will risk their money. So it appears that the moon rocket will have to be a government project.

But governments also have a way of wanting to get something for the money they spend. Of what use would a trip to the moon be to any government? Not very much.

Then do we have to give up the idea of a trip to the moon? No. The trip to the moon might easily come about as a by-product of another project in which a government would be very much interested: a station in space, or man-made moon.

From such a station it would be possible to observe everything that takes place on the

1

ground—for peaceful purposes as well as for military reasons. A possible enemy could not build a military base in secrecy. He could not concentrate his fleet without being observed. Nobody could prepare for war without everybody else's knowledge. And in case of war the space station could not only continue to serve as an observation post, it might also actively aid the fighting by guiding long-range missiles from their firing point to their target.

So the defense departments of the various governments would be much interested in having a station in space. In fact, the United States Army has already said that it is interested, and if one government starts building such a station, several others will have to try it for their own defense.

The station in space may be a lot nearer than anybody now thinks. Once it is set up, the trip to the moon will be comparatively easy and not very expensive.

The First Step

The main reason a space station would be so expensive to build is that it is not one job in itself, like building a barn. It is only the final product of a great development.

Building the space station actually began with the building of the first modern rocket. That in itself was a long and complicated job. Engineers had to worry about the proper shape for both the rocket and the rocket motor. Chemists had to think about the fuels to use. And it was not just a question of finding the most powerful fuel. The most powerful fuel might well be something poisonous and therefore hard to handle. Or it could be a very expensive substance requiring rare raw materials. Or it might be something which just cannot be stored.

So the chemists had to find out which fuel was cheapest and most powerful, in addition to being easy to handle and easy to make in large quantities. Plus a half-dozen other considerations. They have settled for three main fuels. One is alcohol, which is burned with liquid oxygen. Another is a liquid called aniline, which is burned with nitric acid. The third is a kind of kerosene which can be burned with either liquid oxygen or nitric

acid, though it burns better with oxygen.

The engineers, after looking at all the metals available, have settled for a few of them. The outer skin of the rocket is usually aluminum, for the sake of lightness. The rocket motor is either ordinary so-called "mild" steel (a type of steel that is not brittle) or stainless steel. The engineers will probably also make use in the future of a metal called titanium. This is almost as strong as steel, stands heat well and is lighter than steel. But so far aluminum and steel have been doing well.

The rocket engineers have known all along that the first step toward the building of the space station would be to send rockets above the atmosphere. This they succeeded in doing in 1949.

But quite a number of experts said that the simple shooting of a rocket to the fringes of the atmosphere and beyond was not really the first step. Such shots would be made even if the goal were only a long-range missile. The first real step into space, they said, would be a shot which put something into an orbit around the earth. The rocket should stay in space for a while—perhaps just a week, maybe a month or two, or possibly even a year.

This step was taken in the fall of 1957 when Russian rocket experts shot the first two artificial satellites into such orbits. Because they were Russian these two satellites were not called "orbital rockets" (which is the normal term) or even "artificial satellites." Instead, they were given the Russian name for an artificial satellite, which is *sputnik* (pronounced "spootnick").

The first sputnik was fired on October 4, 1957; the second on November 3, 1957. The first one weighed 184 pounds while the second one weighed about 1,000 pounds. But they were not alike, even if one disregards the difference in weight. However, before explaining the difference between the two sputniks, we must first discuss step-rockets.

It is quite obvious that a rocket holding a greater amount of fuel in its tanks can travel faster than one which holds less fuel. The more fuel there is to be burned, the faster the rocket will be traveling when all of its fuel has been used up. But of course there is a limit to this. If too much fuel were packed into a rocket it would grow so heavy that it could not lift itself off the ground.

Motors in nose section of step rocket cut in as other step, fuel expended, falls back to earth. Takeoff would be planned so that first section would fall harmlessly into sea.

With the fuels now in use, the highest speed that can be expected of a rocket is about one and a half miles *per second*. But that isn't nearly enough speed to make an orbit around the earth. For a rocket to be an orbital rocket two things are necessary. First, it must climb to a point above the atmosphere. (This climb does not need to be vertical. It can be—and usually is—done at a slant.) Then the rocket must move parallel to the ground and achieve a speed of a little more than four and a half miles per second.

Now how can this be done if your best rocket can go at the rate of only one and a half miles? This is where the step principle comes in.

Suppose you place a smaller rocket in the nose of the large rocket. Then you figure out a way to make the big rocket burn up all its fuel before the smaller rocket is ignited. If the smaller rocket is already moving at the rate of one and a half miles per second before it starts burning, by the time it has used up its own fuel it will be traveling at the rate of three miles per second.

By this method, a triple rocket, called a three-step or three-stage rocket, can come up to satellite speed. This is just what was done by the Russians. The rockets used were three-stage rockets and the third stage got into an orbit around the earth.

But there is more to it than that. On top of the third rocket (or in its nose) is the artificial satellite. It is a container which holds scientific instruments. It also holds a tiny radio

transmitter which radios the findings of the instruments to the ground, and batteries to power the transmitter. This package of instruments is usually round, like a ball.

Now this instrument package can be left with the third stage, or the two can be made to separate from each other. If they are to separate, the instrument package can be mounted on a spring which is released when the rocket is in the orbit.

In the first sputnik the Russian scientists had the instrument package separate itself from the third-stage rocket so that both revolved around the earth separately. The second sputnik was left in one piece.

Now that the orbital rocket is a reality, it will be followed by other orbital rockets and other artificial satellites. These will be better (as scientific research instruments) or bigger, or both. They will supply the engineers with the information which is still needed.

The next big step will be an orbital rocket with a man in it. He will circle around the planet for a day or two, then enter into the atmosphere again and land. This may be accomplished in a few years from now. In the meantime, of course, the chemists will keep searching for fuels and one day they will no doubt find one which is cheap, not dangerous to handle, and more powerful than any we have now.

If such a fuel is found it may be possible to go into an orbit with a two-stage rocket. We do not need such a fuel to build the space station, but it would make things easier.

Crewless two-step orbital rocket roars up from desert launching site. Telemetering devices in nose section will send data back to earth.

The Supply Ship

The station in space is by no means a copy of the orbital rocket, and building it will require the solution of a number of new problems.

One that must be solved before we can even begin building the space station is the problem of the supply ship. If men are going to live on the station they will have to eat. There isn't any method now known by which they could grow their own food out there, so the food will have to come from the earth. This will necessitate a supply ship, which will run out to the station and back.

This supply ship will be much more difficult to design and build than the orbital rocket. The orbital rocket, without wings or steering gear, can be quite simple. The supply ship will require both wings and steering gear. After it has carried supplies out to the space station it will have to return and make a landing on earth before it can make another trip. Each trip will be very expensive, so the supply ship will have to be very large, probably larger than any airplane we now have. As many supplies as possible must be carried in order to keep down the number of trips. All this means a great deal more than just adding wings and steering gear to an orbital rocket.

It means that there must be an airtight cabin for the pilot and crew. This cabin will require air conditioning. There must also be radio and radar gear for piloting the ship. When the supply ship returns to earth it will be very light for its size. The rocket fuel will have been used up in getting to the station and the supplies will have been left in the orbit. The supply ship probably could land at any large airport.

Crewmen raft materials for space station up from hold of supply ship. Swivel-mounted compressed air nozzles, clamped to equipment, act as "outboard motors."

The supply ship takes off. When sufficient speed is built up on launching track, ram jets may lift ship

The supply ship will have to be air tight. On reaching the space station, an air-tight chamber will connect the ship with an airlock on the station. Passengers will pass through this into the satellite.

One thing not needed by the supply ship will be a crane or any other machine for handling heavy cargo. When the station is reached, the ship, the station, and everything in them will have practically no weight. Using just one hand, a man will be able to carry out the heaviest cases or pieces of metal.

What will the supply ship carry? Frozen food, of course. A little water, too, but not much; used water can be purified at the station and used again. Probably there will be some compressed air in cylinders, because the station will lose a small amount of air every time an airlock is opened. There will also be a need for more air as new rooms are built into the station. Construction materials and tools of all kinds will go out by the supply ship. In fact, they will be its main cargo.

The supply ship will probably be shaped like an airplane because it will be an airplane when landing on earth. Although it won't

off rocket-propelled undercarriage. The rocket motors will cut in later.

require the speed of the orbital rocket, it will come close to it. One of the reasons for building the orbital rocket first is that once it is built, many of the problems of the supply ship, especially those concerning fuel, will be solved.

When the supply ship returns to the earth from the station, it will probably have to circle the earth all the way around in order to come into the air at a long easy slant. Otherwise it would be burned up, as meteors are. The problem in going out is to go fast enough; the problem in coming back is to come slowly enough.

No matter how the supply ship is built, we can learn a lot from it long before we build the station in space or try to fly to the moon with a human cargo. The supply ship can make several flights out into space and return with a crew. The experience of these men will add to the information furnished by the orbital rocket. The first space pilots will get their licenses on supply ships; that is, they will be truck drivers.

Battery-driven "tankettes" may be used on moon. Pneumatic hammers, drills and mechanical arms could be operated from inside revolving turret.

At the Clothing Shop

Along with the supply ship, the problem of the space suit must be solved before we can even begin to build the station in space. The station will be of no use unless men can work outside it, building it up to larger size than when it left the earth, and making repairs on the outer surface.

The station will have to be a very narrow torpedo shape when it leaves the earth, in order to save fuel while passing through the air. But once it gets into its orbit as an artificial moon, the torpedo shape will not be needed. Furthermore, the most useful features of the station will be its observatories—one looking toward the earth, and one looking outward toward the stars. These observatories will need coatings of glass or plastic. Such materials are not strong enough to be part of the surface of an object traveling through the air at a speed of five miles a second. Therefore, the observatories ought to be built into the station after it is in place. For these building operations, the men will need space suits.

A really good and workable space suit is a device which still has to be invented. But engineers do not have to start from scratch since they have already designed and built suits which bear some similarity to the space suit.

Perhaps the earliest device that can be said to bear a similarity to the space suit is the diving suit which was perfected about sixty years ago. But the resemblance between the diving suit and the space suit is really quite small. In both cases the man inside the suit has to be provided with air for breathing. But that is the only important similarity. The wearer of a diving suit is under high water pressure which grows worse the deeper he goes. For this reason the air pressure inside his suit has to match the water pressure outside his suit. Also, the water around the diver is usually very cold, so there is the problem of keeping the man warm inside the diving suit.

In space, conditions are entirely different. Space is a vacuum, hence there will be nothing outside the space suit when it is actually worn in space. For this reason the air pressure in the suit does not need to be very high. It can even be lower than the normal air pressure we have on the ground. The only problem is to bring enough oxygen to the man inside. If the engineers, for some reason of their own, do not want to use the normal air pressure of 14 pounds per square inch, they can use air with a lower pressure but with more oxygen than is found in normal air.

The temperature problem is different, too. Since the man in the diving suit is surrounded by cold water, he has to be kept warm. The man in the space suit, on the other hand, is surrounded by a vacuum. A vacuum is not hot and not cold; it simply has no temperature at all. So the man in the space suit will not receive any temperature of any kind from his immediate surroundings.

His problem is entirely different. While in space he will receive heat from the sun's radiation. This will warm his suit on the side which is turned toward the sun. On the side which is away from the sun he will lose some of that heat by radiating it away into space, much as a radiator loses heat by radiating it into a cold room.

How much heat he will receive from the sun and how much he will radiate will depend on several factors, of which the color of the suit will be the most important. A dark suit will keep more heat than a light suit. The texture of the suit will also affect the amount of heat received and radiated. Smooth metal heats up differently than rough fabric. The man inside the suit produces heat, too. For example, when you are in a closed telephone booth you soon begin to feel warmer, even on a cold day. It is your own body heat which warms up the booth.

So a space suit will not need heating—that will be done by the man inside. It will be in need of cooling, instead.

Some of the suits which have been built for test pilots flying experimental planes to high altitudes have probably come close to the real space suit. (There have even been some experimental models of space suits, but these are still quite awkward and uncomfortable.) Like the real space suit, the high-altitude suits have to protect the man from low pressure and supply him with oxygen. They do not need a cooling unit for the simple reason that in these experimental planes the whole cabin is air-conditioned.

Because of the experience of these test pilots we can figure out what a space suit must do. We know that the man inside the suit will produce carbon dioxide, moisture and heat. So the carbon dioxide he exhales must be removed, because if it were permitted to accumulate, it would put him to sleep after a while. The man also exhales a lot of water, which condenses inside the suit as moisture. This would not do any real harm to the man but would make him feel very uncomfortable. So the water vapor must be removed, too, along with the heat which he produces.

Since the man is not likely to be in the suit for more than a number of hours, there is no need to feed him. But he may need some water to drink. And of course he needs oxygen to breathe.

So we know the suit must be air-conditioned; it must have a device for removing moisture and another device for removing the carbon dioxide. It would be best if all this equipment were placed on the wearer's back outside the suit so that it could be exchanged quickly. This applies as well to the bottles with oxygen for breathing.

Since there is no air in space to carry sound, the space suit must have a built-in radio similar to the army's walkie-talkie. Also, the helmet must have a kind of window for looking out. This will probably be a fairly narrow slit in the metal of the helmet, covered with a special kind of glass or a transparent plastic.

Air-lock door open, space-suited repair crew goes into action. Man on left has just fired a magnetized, line-carrying projectile to damaged ship. Oxygen tanks, CO₂ absorption apparatus, batteries and radio are packed on back. Tools carried by man in foreground are operated from inside sleeve of suit. Sunvisors and magnetized boots will be necessary.

Takeoff! Smoke, flame and dust billow out as the space station rocket gathers speed. Forward section will never return to earth, but will circle it, a man-made moon, forever.

The Space Station Gets Ready to Take Off

Imagine that we have solved the problems of the supply ship and the space suit. Now we are ready to start work on the space station. In the beginning this will be a rocket, but much bigger than the orbital rocket.

It will have to carry all kinds of instruments and tools; there will be water and air and food; there will be things like books. Most important, there will be the people themselves.

It will need an engine to furnish power for working machines, for cleaning the air, for electricity and various other things.

And, finally, the space station will have to carry building materials that will change it from a rocket to a real station. Of course, the supply ship can bring most of these up later, but some will have to go on the first trip. Large amounts of food and water will add considerable weight. The air that must be taken along will not weigh anything itself, but it will have to be carried in compressed form and the containers will weigh a good deal.

All told, for a space station with a crew of four it will not be safe to count on a total weight of much less than 100 tons. This will be the weight when the station reaches the end of its journey and becomes a real artificial moon. When it takes off from earth its weight will be very much greater, most of it in fuel.

The German V-2 started its journey as a fourteen-ton rocket to deliver only one ton of explosives when it struck. And it was intended to come back to earth, not to make the long hard journey out into space.

Over nine tons of the V-2's weight was in fuel. Even with far better fuels than those we now have, the fuel proportion for a trip to space would be at least this high. That is, the rocket which is to become a 100-ton space station will weigh nearly 1000 tons at takeoff, and probably 1,500 tons.

This is a very big rocket indeed, as tall as a skyscraper, and it will have to be bigger still if we use a two-stepper. But if the supply ship has already made several trips out into space, it ought not to be too hard to build it the right way. And sending up a very big rocket will be an advantage in one way. The huge fuel tanks and the beams supporting them will become building materials for increasing the size of the station once it is on the job.

Nearing completion, two-step space station rocket towers over temporary construction town.

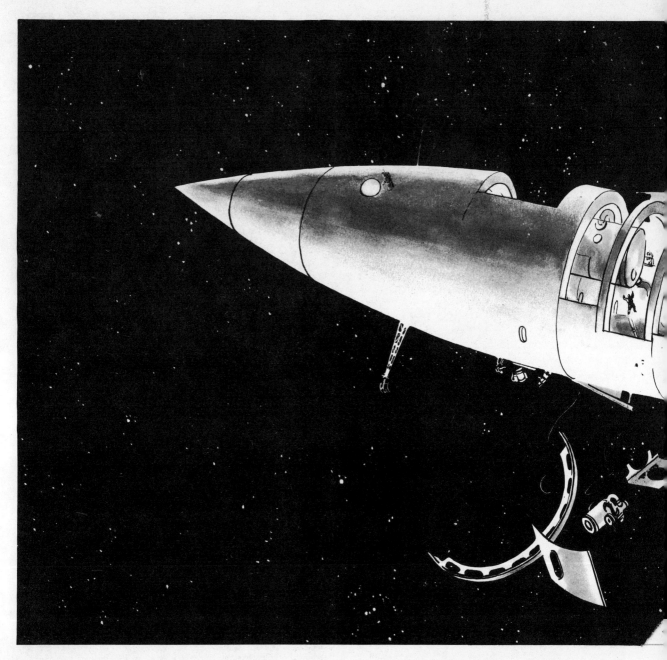

Orbital velocity once attained, work on the space station begins. Now useless fuel tanks and stabilizers will be dismantled and the material used. Rocket motors will be jettisoned or sent back to earth on supply ship.

Life in the Space Station

The space rocket has now fallen into its orbit and the crew is ready to begin work on turning the rocket into a station. Let us call it "Project X."

Down on earth people can look up into the night sky and see a new and very bright star, bright because it is so close to the earth. It can be calculated how far out the station

18

will be. The best distance is 1075 miles. (Farther out, it would revolve around the earth more slowly, but it would be harder to bring up supplies.) Even a 100-ton station would be visible at that distance and it will grow steadily larger.

The air purifying machines are now running and life on the station has begun. What is that life like? The first thing the crew notices after the station is in its orbit, is that nothing seems to have any weight.

What is called weight is caused by gravity. This pulls everything in the world, or in the air above it, toward the exact center of the earth.

The space station has now become a little world of its own. Everything in it is being drawn toward its center, but only very gently because the station is so small compared to the earth. This loss of weight will make people feel queer for a while and queer things will happen. But the doctors tell us it won't hurt them, at least until they have been there for some time.

Every object in the station will float. You won't have to hold a book in order to read it; you merely hang it in the air in front of you. But be careful not to give it even a gentle push. It will sail slowly toward the other side of the room and have to be brought back. You will also have to be careful about putting things away in drawers and on racks.

Water can't be carried in bottles. It will come in round plastic containers and when you want a drink you will have to suck it out through a straw. When you want to cook something in water, it will have to be done in a pressure cooker and on an electric stove.

No one will be allowed to smoke, because smoking uses up the air too fast.

You ought to sleep well on the station in space. In fact, after you get used to it, you probably won't want a bed at all. You just lie down in the air anywhere, probably snapping a wall connection into some kind of belt to keep from floating out of the room and getting in the way of other people. Naturally, you won't want to wear your magnetic shoes while sleeping. It would give you the feeling of sleeping while you are standing up.

When you move about the station you will do it by pushing yourself away from one of the walls. It will probably take some time to learn to do this with the right amount of force to keep from bumping your head on the other side or landing in the wrong position. In fact, there won't be any sides or top or bottom in the station. There will just be walls all around, and the direction you are standing in will always be "up." This will make one thing pretty easy. You can live in much less space because the upper walls and ceiling, which are wasted in a room, can be used to hold things like bookcases, tool racks or drawers where clothes are kept. If two people are "standing" with their feet on opposite sides of a room, each will look upside down to the other, and both will be right.

There won't be any day or night on the station any more than there is on a submarine. Even day and night on the earth will appear strange to the people on the station. The speed necessary for the rocket to become a station is such that it will be going right around the earth in a little over two hours, and people in Project X will see both the day and night side on every trip around. There will have to be some special kind of clock, which hasn't been invented yet, just for Project X.

One of the real problems of the station will be getting rid of waste, such as garbage. You can't just pitch it out the airlock, for it would be attracted by the small gravity of the station and stick to the outside. So there will have to be waste-containers which are shot away from the station by rocket power when full.

From the very first moment when the station reaches its position, there will have to be a ventilation system running. Without gravity the used air breathed out by the crew members and the perspiration from their bodies would surround them in a fine misty cloud of useless air. They would soon smother in their own waste products unless there were something to carry these off.

With its orbital velocity matched to that of the space station, a supply rocket starts unloading. Materials may be floated down—or ship may dock on station.

Building up Project X

The first step in turning the orbital rocket into a real space station is to set up the dock for the supply ship. This will be quite a tricky piece of design. It will have to have very strong walls, because it is too much to expect that the supply ship can be aimed from the earth to hit the station in exactly the right place. She will probably have to over-shoot a little, braking down by firing rockets, and the walls of the dock will have to be strong enough to stand it.

Once the two ships — the orbital rocket and the supply ship — are near enough, they they will attract each other by gravity. This will cause them to float gently together. This period, during which the supply ship and the space station are coming together, is likely to last as long as all the rest of the trip. The gravity of the two machines is so small that the approach will be very slow. The trip up from the earth will take just one hour and a few minutes. The drift-in may well take twice as much time.

On the side of the station opposite the dock the next building will be erected. This will be a rocket chamber that fires a blast to correct the position of the station when the supply ship comes in. Otherwise the braking blast fired by the supply ship might set the station spinning. If it once started spinning it would never stop because there is no air to slow down the motion. In fact, it will probably be a good idea to set up a series of "spin tubes" all around the station.

The next most important rooms of Project X will be the two observatories. An observatory contains a great deal of heavy equipment and it takes a long time to build one on earth. But building in space has advantages that make the process much simpler. Huge beams and castings that would have to be handled with a crane on earth, will weigh so very little that a man can easily move them into position by hand. It will only be necessary for him to give himself a stronger shove than usual from one of

Once contact between magnetized boots and deck has been broken, men will be able to float around. Here worker guides a girder into place in observatory shell. Construction material can be very light.

the walls. It is very important to get the observatories set up quickly both for watching the weather on earth and bringing the supply ship in.

When this is done the station will have a strange lumpy look, with the dock growing out of one side, the spin tube out of the other, and the observatories bulging from top and bottom like huge warts. The beautiful smooth shape of the original rocket will be gone. This doesn't matter in space, where there is no air to resist movement, and the streamline shape is of no help.

After the observatories are completed, the crew can start to enlarge the station with more rooms for living quarters. These rooms will be built on all sides of the original rocket, and will look very odd. It is important to give them a shape that will be strong but will use the least possible amount of building material. At the same time the shape must be one that will afford greatest possible space inside. No space can be wasted, for waste space means waste air, and air must be brought up from the earth.

Finally, the shape should be one that will allow additional rooms to be built without tearing apart those already set up. The right shape for this is six-sided, like the cell of a honeycomb. Such a figure is called a hexagonal prism. A perfectly round room would make better use of the space inside, but it would waste space between the rooms, and we need flat walls for placing things.

Inside, this room will not look like anything on earth, because all the walls will be in use. The bed may be directly overhead, the library on one angled wall, the tool kit on another. Or it may look that way until you start walking up one of the side walls, when the library will be under your feet and the bed on one side.

Finished station bristles with radio and radar. Docks, air locks, observatories bulge up from the flat decks. Giant reflectors furnish heat for power. The space ship for the moon trip is under construction on one deck.

The supply ship takes a meteor hit. Airtight doors inside the hull have sealed off the pierced compartments. Outside, crewmen survey the damage, and a "trouble-scooter" jets up to make repairs.

Gravity and Meteorites

It may develop that carrying metal to a place 1,075 miles from the earth will be much too expensive. In that case, after the parts of the original rocket have been used up or put aside for structures that must necessarily be made of metal, the rest of the station would have to be built of something else. The best material would be some kind of lightweight plastic which could be filled with air to take the shape wanted.

There is another problem that is closely related to the lives and comfort of those who will live on the station. Some people think that men cannot stand being totally without weight for a long time. If this turns out to be true the station will have to have some kind of artificial gravity of its own. This can be done by setting the station spinning, so that what is called centrifugal force takes the place of gravity. It would be easy enough to start it to spin.

But this kind of artificial gravity would be the most useful in the part of the station that was spinning the fastest—that is, the part farthest from the center. So the living quarters would be placed as far out from the center as possible. This would mean that the finished station would look like a huge doughnut, with the power unit which had been the body of the original rocket at the center, hanging like a huge egg on thin hollow beams. These beams would hold passages running from the living rooms to the workshops.

Although the gravity produced by spinning would be very small, we would lose some of the advantages of being without weight. To a man in the living rooms, the working space would always be "up," but when he got there, there would be no "down"!

There is a source of danger that we have not yet considered: meteorites. Many thousands of these pebble-like objects come speeding through space and strike the earth each day. Most of them are less than half an inch through. They are drawn to the earth by the pull of its gravity. This is so great that meteorites hit the earth at a speed of seven miles a second, just exactly the speed a space ship needs to get away from earth for good.

Many meteorites strike the earth's atmosphere with a much higher speed than seven miles per second. This is due to the fact that they had a velocity of their own long before they came near enough to the earth to be attracted by it. But the space station will be much too small (by comparison) to attract any meteorites into the path of its own gravity.

There is just one chance of meteorite damage. This would occur if a large meteorite happened to be traveling toward some big body—probably the earth—along a line that would bring it into the station head-on. There is about as much chance of this as there is of a head-on collision between two airplanes. But even these sometimes happen, and we must prepare for it.

The original rocket, of course, will have sides that are stout and thick enough to resist any meteorite it is likely to meet, but when work is started on the living rooms, their sides will be of thin metal or plastic. They will need protection against tiny meteorites that might let the air out.

Fortunately most meteorites are tiny. The vast majority of them are smaller even than grains of sand. Their size is about the same as that of the tiny grains of the finest flour or the best quality of face powder. If it were possible for you to have a large coal shovel full of these average-sized meteorites, there would most likely be only one which would be large enough to be easily visible without a magnifying lens.

If the meteorites were to run into the space station, the effect would not be like that of gunshot. It would be more like what engineers call sandblasting. (This is a method of blowing finely ground sand by means of an air jet.)

For a few hours this would be harmless, but in time such sandblasting would weaken the walls of the space station. However, there is a way to avert this danger. If the wall or skin of the space station were protected by extra sheets of metal on the outside, these metal sheets would take the brunt of the impact of the dust meteorites. In time these metal sheets would wear out and have to be replaced. But the skin of the station would not be damaged.

If lack of gravity proves to have serious physical effects on crew, space station may be built like this. Observatories will be in central hub, living and working quarters in revolving rim.

Building the Space Ship

Once enough living spaces have been built to keep the crew comfortable, more people will go out in the supply ship. Let us go out, too, and help with the work of getting the station really operating.

The first step is to set up a power plant to replace the expensive fuel-using engine that arrived while Project X was still a rocket. This is much easier than it sounds. All we need is a large mirror of some shiny metal—nickel would be best—shaped like a soup plate. This will be arranged to concentrate the reflection on a tank of water.

The mirror will be set on pivots so that it will always face the sun. The sun's energy, gathered and used in this way, has produced enough heat to melt a brick down on the earth. Out here in space, with no air to interfere, we can turn the water into steam as fast as we wish. The steam can then drive a

steam engine to give us all the power and light we want. From this time on the power supply will be free, and the same sun boiler will serve as the water purifying unit.

After we have built the station to its final shape, we are ready to begin work on the next project. If the station has been built by the army or air force, as is most likely, the first job of Project X will be setting up guided missiles and trying them out. Of course there will be experiments with radar and radio and such things as radiation in space while the station is still being built to its final shape. There will probably also be a few experiments in running the station faster and slower, nearer and farther from the earth.

It is just possible that before the station is finished someone will already have taken off for the moon directly from the earth. But it is not very probable. Even with better

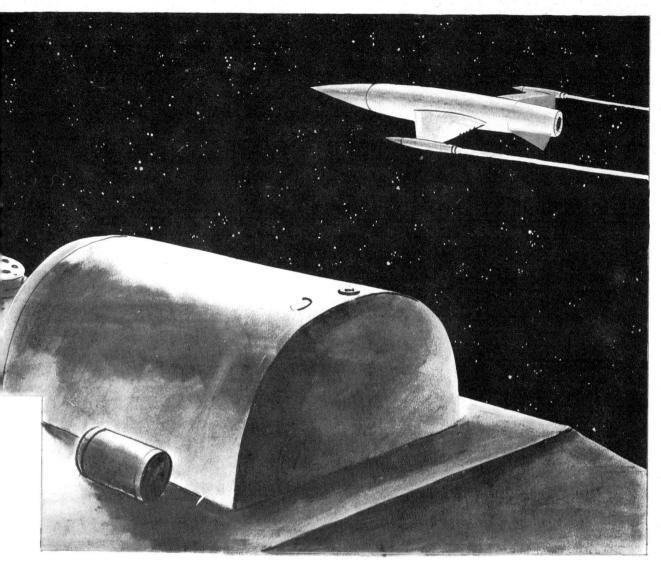

The spherical exploration ship takes shape. Lack of weight will mean ease of construction. "Fish-pole" cranes, with magnets for hooks, guide large pieces into place. Magnetic clamps will hold equipment to deck, to stop its floating away.

fuels it would take a three-step rocket to reach the moon, much larger than the one for setting up Project X. And even with such a rocket, there would be no chance of landing on the moon, because it would take still another rocket to get away again. This would call for a four-step rocket, and probably not even the government of a large country would want to pay for it.

The trip to the moon does not promise to give very important results, except to the military. However, for scientific purposes it is the nearest object in the skies and the easiest trip. Once men have reached the moon and come back, visiting the other planets of

the solar system will be easy.

The first real space ship will be built at Project X for two reasons. One is the cheap power kindly furnished by the sun. The other is that the ship will be quite different from what we think of as a rocket, more resembling the space station itself. Such a space ship would be quite unable to take off from the earth.

It will have no use for wings because there is no air where it is going. It will have no use for outside steering gear. There may be some steering vanes in the jet blasts, but that is all. It can be the shape that gives the most inside space for the least outside space—that is, a ball. It won't need as much fuel as a rocket leaving the earth, not even as much as a supply ship. It won't need thick walls, for the danger of a rough landing on the moon can be taken care of by shock absorbers.

Concerning the arrangements inside the ball, there will probably be a discussion between the space pilots who will operate the ship and the engineers who will build it. The space men will say they want rocket tubes all around the ball, or at least on the two opposite sides. These will help in braking down as they approach the moon or another planet, and in taking off again without having to turn over.

The engineers will say that it's too difficult and expensive to build this way, and that the pilots had better learn how to turn over and ride down on a single rocket jet. The engineers will probably win the argument. They usually do.

Scattered all over the surface of the first moon ship there will be observation lenses. These will be connected with periscopes so the crew can see what's going on outside. The ship will also have radar apparatus.

Probably the ship will not be very large, just big enough for a crew of two. It will be built to connect up with Project X's dock, or with a special dock built on the other side of the space station.

Like the station itself, the moon ship will need an airlock, on the side away from the rocket; it will also need heating and cooling units, and power to operate them. Building the ship will be like building a Project X all over again on a small scale.

The moon ship will need something that a space station does not have—a large gyro installation, placed near the exact center of the ship, to make the necessary turnover on approaching the moon. It will need room for storing space suits, food, water, and sci-

entific instruments. Fitting all these together and getting them into the smallest possible space is going to be tough project for the designers.

Finally, the problem of protecting the space ship against meteorites must be solved. There are two ways of doing this, each with advantages and disadvantages. One is to build the space ship like the softer parts of the station, with a fairly thin surface covered by a blanket of air cells and an aluminum coating. This would have one possible advantage. With such an arrangement it might not be necessary to carry an air purifying unit, for the air around the space ship could be drawn on cell by cell. The used air would be packed away in the same cells for treatment after the ship returned to the station. The disadvantage of this arrangement is that the landing would have to be skillfully made. A hard landing might break right through both sides of the cells. And the moon looks like a very rough place, with plenty of spikey rocks.

On the other hand, a shell thick and heavy enough to take the shock of a hard landing would mean extra weight. It would also require either an air purification unit or a large supply of compressed air, which would mean more weight. This isn't important at the space station, where there isn't any weight, but as soon as the space ship is on the moon, it becomes very important indeed. The larger size of the moon means a greater pull or gravity; greater gravity gives matter greater weight.

Weight is important because fuel is needed to move heavy bodies, and every time fuel is used in a rocket engine things begin to get expensive. A rocket engine burns up fuel very fast, and the need for lifting a large amount of it at the start makes still more fuel necessary. Every time you say "fuel" to a rocket engineer, he begins to shake his head.

A push is sufficient to launch the moon rocket. Once clear of the station, rocket motors will blast the ship on its long voyage.

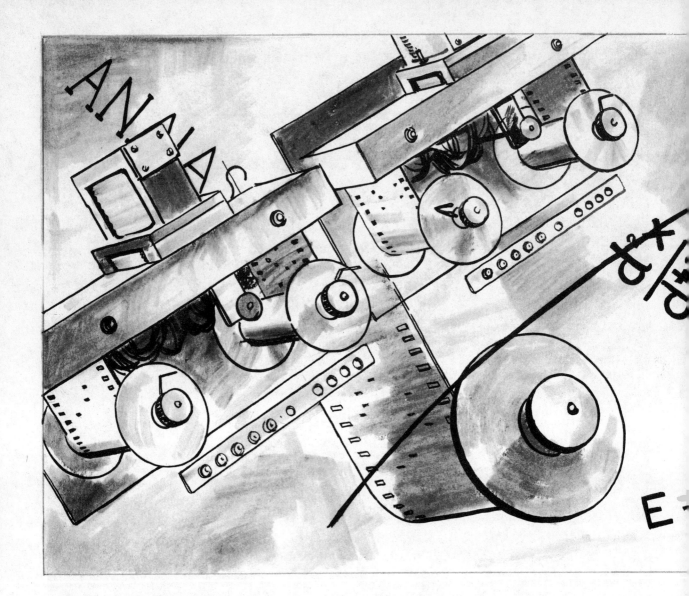

The Takeoff from Project X

Let the engineers decide what system they are going to use in building their big ball. We shall take a look at what happens after it is built.

The route to the moon must first be calculated, and this will be a very difficult task. The takeoff will have to be made at precisely the right split second in time and from precisely the right inch in space. The space ship will be able to change its course, of course, or it wouldn't be of much use. But every time you change course you use up fuel, and every time you use fuel you make

trouble for the engineers. So it's a lot better to make the calculation accurate in the first place.

Astronomers have known for a long time how to make such calculations. These are not especially difficult for somebody who is well versed in mathematics. But they have always been, and still are, very tedious. One such calculation might occupy all the waking time of even a skilled mathematician for six or eight weeks. And it is one thing to figure out, say, the path of a comet after it has disappeared. But when it comes to space

34

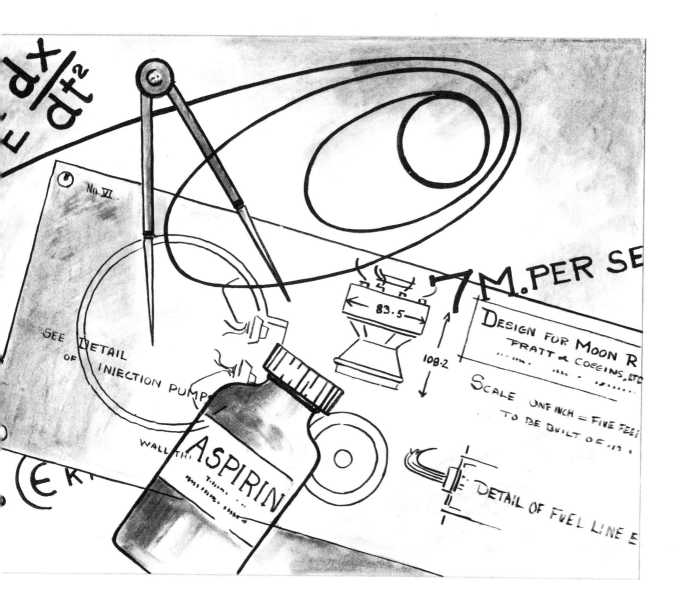

travel more than one calculation is needed. In fact, dozens of them may be needed. And fast!

Here the big electronic computers save the day. They can run off such a calculation in minutes if they have been "set" for it. This setting up may take days or even weeks, but it can be done in advance.

Of course the space station does not have to carry such a computer. It can be on the ground. And the space station, or the space ship, will radio its problems to the computing center, which will radio back the proper course to be followed.

It will probably pay to send a small unmanned rocket to the moon first to test things out, just as we sent up the orbital rocket before building the space station. This time we don't want it to miss and fall into an orbit. We will want to know if it makes a direct hit; so it will carry something to make a bright flash when it strikes the dark side of the moon. It has been calculated that a 100-pound charge of flashlight powder going off in this way could be seen from the earth. Much less could be seen from Project X, so sending the rocket will be no problem. It would be easy.

The moon rocket has landed safely on her hydraulic "spider legs" and the work of surveying

and exploring has begun. Scientist in foreground is using an ore detector.

The Trip To The Moon

Let us suppose that all the calculations have been made. The test rocket has been fired, and it showed up beautifully. Down on earth people have seen the great flare at the space station as the first real space ship took off. Launching the space ship from the station was much easier than sending off the supply ship. Some of the station's crew came out to push it a few feet away from the station. Then they turned on the space ship's rockets. A great explosion followed, but this did not hurt the station for two reasons. First, the big ball was not touching the station when the rockets went off. Secondly, there was no air to pass along the blast. On earth an explosion sets up violent air waves that damage things in their paths.

Now it is very quiet aboard the ship. There are only the sounds from the instruments and the ventilating system and the voices of the passengers, for after the very brief and noisy blast which started the ship on her way the engine has cut off.

It is 239,000 miles from the earth to the moon. Project X is less than 1,100 miles from the earth but all the journey except the very start will be made by coasting.

The first moon travelers haven't begun to put on their space suits yet. There will be plenty of time for that because, in contrast to the one hour which it takes to get from the ground to the space station, it will take about five days to go from the space station to the moon. The explorers will be able to check their course carefully by observations of the apparent size of the moon and by other means. And they can get instructions from the computing center on earth. The landing can be left to automatic machinery which will measure the distance by radar and switch the rocket motors on and off as needed. The explorers will lie in their bunks, strapped down, and wait for the bell signal to tell them that they have landed.

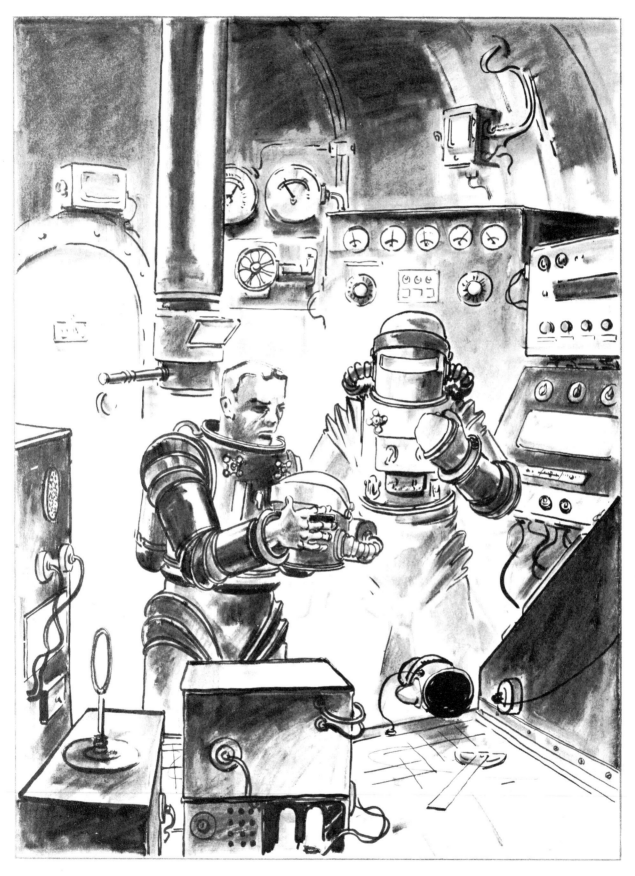

Space suits are put on in readiness for landing. Gear must be carefully checked before entering air lock. Joints in suits must be locked tight, and batteries for heating and "walkie-talkies" tested.

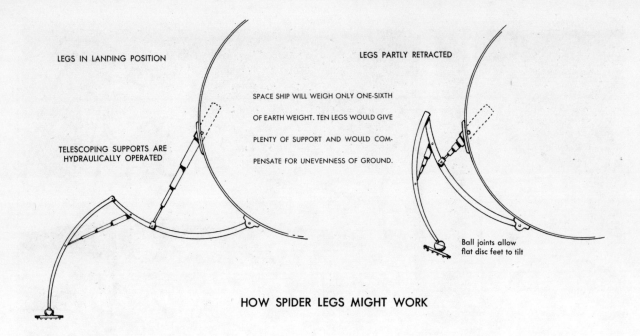

LEGS IN LANDING POSITION

LEGS PARTLY RETRACTED

SPACE SHIP WILL WEIGH ONLY ONE-SIXTH OF EARTH WEIGHT. TEN LEGS WOULD GIVE PLENTY OF SUPPORT AND WOULD COMPENSATE FOR UNEVENNESS OF GROUND.

TELESCOPING SUPPORTS ARE HYDRAULICALLY OPERATED

Ball joints allow flat disc feet to tilt

HOW SPIDER LEGS MIGHT WORK

Seen through a telescope, the moon has a very rough and rugged surface. It looks like a field which has been bombarded by gigantic shells. As a matter of fact that is exactly what it is.

During the many thousands of years since it lost its atmosphere, and doubtless for some time before, the moon has been a target for meteorites, both small and large. They have gone smashing into it with no atmosphere to slow them up, as on the earth, and they have torn the face of the moon to bits. They have dug great craters and scattered the material around the edges to form the mountains of the moon.

These craters look like plains through a telescope, but they are apt to be very rough plains. They are covered with an inch or two of fine dust made up of tiny meteorites, the size of pinheads or smaller.

It is on this surface — uneven, probably rocky, and very dusty — that the space ship must come down. But its navigators cannot allow the outlet, or vent, to touch such a surface. The outlet, at the end of the rocket, is one of the most delicate parts of the engine. If it were to become bruised or clogged with

moon dust, the rocket chamber might blow up when the explorers tried to take off from the moon again. Or the jet might fail to fire in a straight line. In either case, the explorers could never get back to the space station or to earth.

So to keep that rocket vent from actually touching the moon's surface we need a very special arrangement. This will be a series of long curved legs that fold back into the surface of the space ship while it is making the journey. There will be fifteen or twenty of these legs, enough to keep the space ship balanced, no matter how rough the surface on which it lands.

When the radar apparatus tells the explorers that it is time to turn the ship over for a landing, the legs will be let down. They will have two sets of joints, knee-joints with shock-absorbers in them, and ankle joints to take care of the uneven ground. At the bottom of the legs there will be broad feet. When the space ship is standing on the moon it will look like a huge spider, that somehow has grown more legs than a spider should have.

Crewman wheels fuel tank from cave, as moon-to-earth missile is readied for firing.

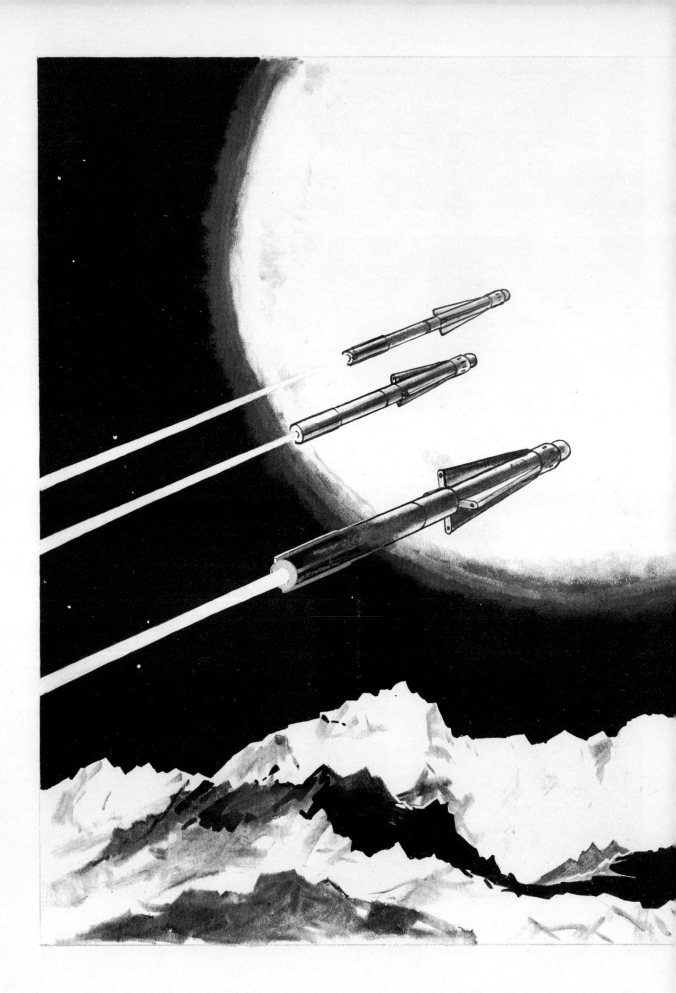

A shoal of interceptor rockets roars up toward an incoming earth-to-moon missile. Blinding flash over mountains in distance shows where a second missile has been successfully intercepted and destroyed.

The Explorers on the Moon

We need not expect too much from that moon trip except that it will give people experience in handling real space ships and lead to setting up a base on the moon. We won't know exactly what the moon is made of until someone goes there. But scientific instruments give us a pretty good idea. The chances are that most of it is nothing but a big chunk of granite, or something similar. Granite is a good building material, but it is not very useful for anything else. If there are really valuable minerals on the moon, it will take time and exploration to find them.

However, there is another reason for making the expensive trip to the moon besides just the fun of the trip itself. You remember we began by saying that the only people who would find it worth while paying for the space station would be one of the defense departments. Now it is just possible to use this station as a military base, but only just possible. It will be very difficult to hit an earthly target with a guided missile because the station is moving so very fast. Of course, matters could be improved by sending the station out farther. A station 4,000 miles out would take four hours to spin round the earth, and one 7,700 miles out would take seven hours. But this is not much use, because of the amount of fuel the supply ship would use every time it went out to the greater distance.

And if the supply ship can go up to the station, enemies can always send up guided rockets to attack it. Defenses could be worked out, but there is a chance they might not be good enough. It would be much cheaper for an enemy to send a dozen or twenty giant rockets up to shoot down the space station than to build one himself.

Therefore we only really want a station in space as a station, while we are getting ready to set up a base on the moon. That is what we really need for defense purposes. The station on the moon would be pretty safe against any kind of attack from earth. It would take hours for the fastest rocket to reach the moon. Long before it arrived, radar could detect its coming. An intercepting rocket would be fired at it. The intercepter doesn't have to make a direct hit either. It would only need to explode near the attacking rocket to throw it off course. It could be very much smaller and cheaper than the attacking rocket, and guided missiles fired from the moon against a target on earth would be almost impossible to stop.

So the first trip to the moon will be made to explore for a place where a military base can be set up.

As soon as the space travelers have put on their suits, let down a folding ladder and reached the ground, they will start searching. After examining samples of moon dust, they may find that some of the rocks are useful. But what they are really looking for is a place to build a base.

What kind of place is needed? The best location would be a huge cave near the bottom of one of the moon mountains. The base will need an observatory, which will have to be above the surface of the ground. It will also need a solar power station and radar instruments, all of which will have to be outside, too. But the main works of the base ought to be underground, a long way underground, because of the continuous bombardment by meteorites.

The explorers will be looking for a big cave, well down toward the base of one of the moon mountains. Unfortunately their chances of finding such a cave are not good.

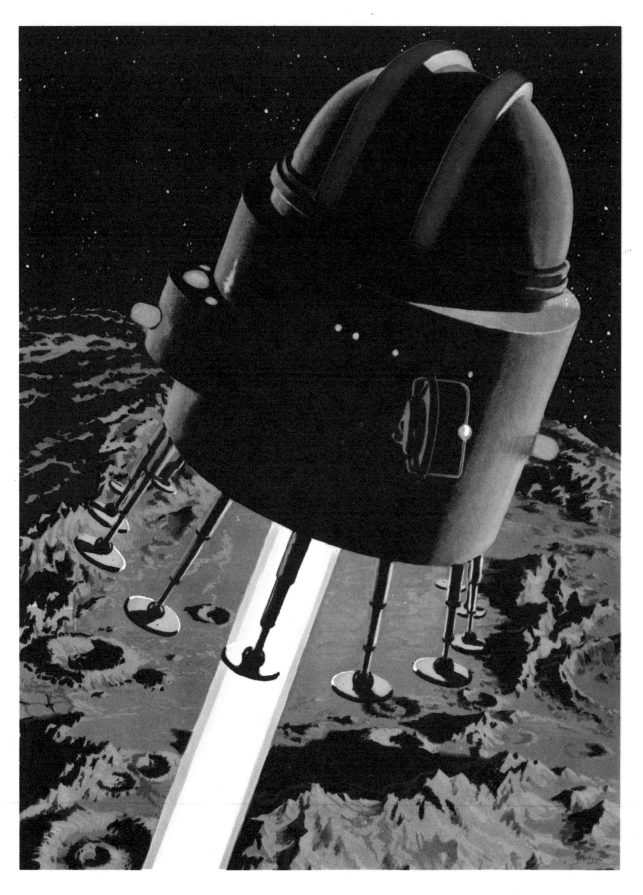

Braking down on moon. Base ship will be dismantled to build moon-base. Observatory will be re-erected on mountain top.

The dismantled ship lies behind temporary camp. Completed base will be in caves like one under observatory.

Most caves on earth are the result of water wearing away rocks. The moon has no water in liquid form, though it may have had at one time. However, it is doubtful that there was time for water to hollow out caves before the moon lost its air and froze, thousands of years ago.

It would be a happy discovery if the explorers could find a large cave, filled with ice. That would save the trouble of carrying water all the way out from earth. More probably they will have to go back to Project X with a report that a cave will have to be dug out. On the next trip out, a working party would begin to build the base.

Building the Moon Base

Building the moon base will be quite a job, and it will call for a much bigger space ship than the first one. Not that the first space ship, which we shall call the "Explorer," will be useless after having made her trip. She can still be used as a messenger, a supply ship that will travel from Project X to the moon base. Later on, after the moon

base is set up, the "Explorer" can attempt to make trips to Mars or Venus.

The space ship that is to set up the moon base will have to be as big as Project X itself —or at least as big as that station was when it took off from earth as a rocket. It will have to carry all the things the space station needs —supplies of frozen food, water, air, fuel,

engines, instruments, space suits — and in addition, quantities of tools. The size of the ship will depend upon the number of people in the working party, but there is no use in making it too small, because more people will have to go out anyway.

As this is a working ship, whose parts will be used in building the base, it will not need as many folding legs as the "Explorer," only enough to assure a safe landing. The frame-work and beams of the base ship will become the beams inside the cave; the doors will be the doors of the cave; the telescopes and radar instruments will be part of the base. The whole story of building the base will be one of gradually taking the ship apart.

Down on earth the parts of the ship will have been shaped with this in mind. Then they will be taken out to the space station to be put together.

The shape they will finally take is not important. When we built Project X, we had to make it a torpedo shape to go up through the air. The "Explorer" was ball-shaped to make it as small as possible on the outside, but to give it as much space as possible inside. The ship that will fly out to set up the moon base will not have to go through air, and there is no special reason for saving space in it. So it will be the shape that will allow the best use of the parts in building the base. It may even look like a flying box-car.

While they are working on their cave and making it air-tight, the crew of the base will have to live in the moon base ship. For this reason it might pay to make it of several separate rooms, arranged just as they will be when it becomes a base. Then on the moon, the rooms and everything in them can be moved right into the cave.

The cave at the base will be an underground city, rather small at first, because there won't be enough air for a large one. It can be lined with any one of a number of materials to make it air-tight, and it will probably have air-tight doors between the rooms. This arrangement will make it look like the inside of a warship.

Little by little the strange underground city will be built, the furniture moved in, heating and lighting apparatus set up, and air brought in. Later the observatory and the weapons room will be erected.

Air at the Moon Base

At the moon base, there will be a great difference in the way the air supply is handled. On Project X we began with bottled air, and the "Explorer" will continue to use it. Enough bottled air could be carried to last the space station for six months. More could always be delivered by the supply ship, but carrying air back and forth to Project X would be a terrible waste of fuel. So the space station will have to handle its own air problems soon after it is in working order.

Now purifying air is a very difficult business. Almost the only things that will do it are green plants that will break up the poisonous carbon dioxide always present in the air we breathe out.

But the use of ordinary plants to purify the air of the space station would not be very practical. It would take a great many to handle all the air the people there would need. The plant rooms would have to be bigger than all the rest of the station put together.

So the space station will need some other air purification system than just a bed of plants. Is there any such system? Yes, the tiny plants called algae are just as good at converting carbon dioxide into breathable oxygen as their big cousins in the fields. Nearly all algae live in water, but we need water at Project X anyway. So the center of the air purification system will be a big water-tank filled with algae.

The ventilation system can be arranged to pump the carbon dioxide into this tank. As there is no gravity at the station, the carbon dioxide will not bubble through the water as one might expect. The water will have to be stirred constantly by big paddles so the algae can get at the carbon dioxide. This sounds like very harsh treatment, but most algae are tough enough to stand it.

All this would be unnecessary on the moon, where there is plenty of space, and getting still more is just a question of enlarging the cave. It will only be necessary to set

Bright earth-light floods moon landscape. Earth would appear four times as large as moon does to us.

Due to chemical feeding and weak gravity, vegetables grown in hydroponic tanks may attain great size. Lamps will provide synthetic sunlight in caves.

up a system of big greenhouses and connect them with the ventilation system for the base. Whether the dust of the moon's surface would make the right kind of soil for growing plants, we don't know. Probably not. We also know there isn't any other kind of soil on the moon.

But this is not a serious problem. There is a system of growing plants that is known as "hydroponics." The plants are grown in large gravel beds, with water flowing through them, carrying with it the chemicals that plants usually get from soil.

Plants grown by hydroponics are larger and more lush than those grown in the ground. Out on the moon, the plants would have only one-sixth of the earth's gravity to fight, so they would grow even larger and faster. They might turn into something quite different from their earthly ancestors, with big, rich leaves. But that would only make them better for purifying air.

Of course, many of these plants would be part of the food supply of the moon base party. But it would not be wise to count too much on that. When a plant begins to develop very big leaves, it often forgets about its roots. For example, if potatoes or radishes were grown on the moon, the chances are that they would look beautiful above ground, but there wouldn't be much potato or radish. Leafy vegetables like lettuce, on the other hand, would be splendid, and very tender.

It will probably be necessary to put the hydroponic garden underground, too, and bring light to it artificially. The moon base party cannot afford to lose the air and plants that would be gone if the greenhouse were hit by a meteorite.

All this digging and building will take lots of power. But once the sun engine is set up, like the one at Project X, there will be no need to worry about that.

The magazines and weapons room will be deep underground. Missiles might be launched through tubes sunk through the solid rock.

Sun's rays are focused by large reflector on mercury boiler. Vapor will drive engines to furnish electric power.

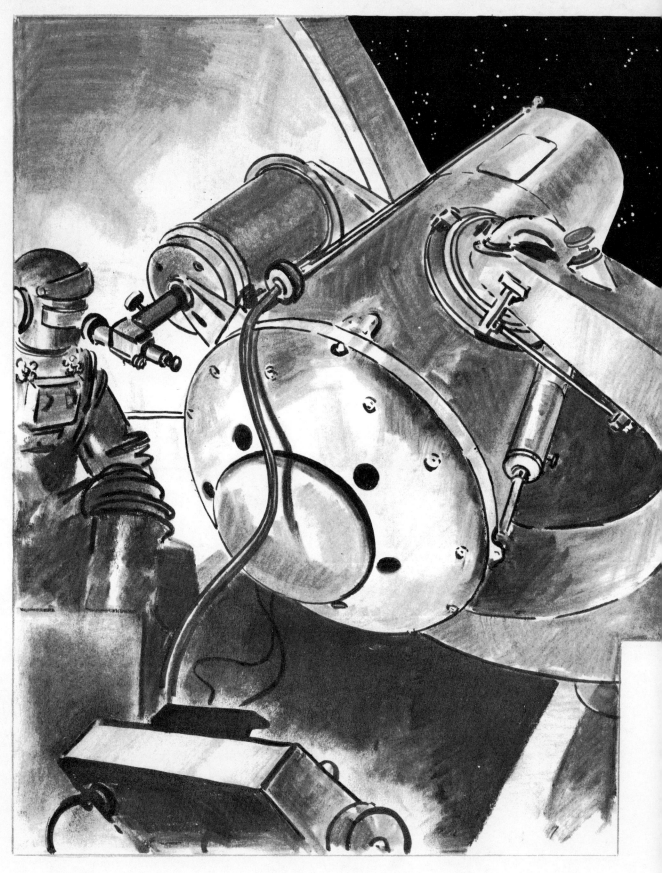

Moon observatory in operation. Space-suited astronomers adjust Schmidt telescopic camera. Lack of atmosphere insures perfect visibility.

After the Moon Base is Working

As soon as the moon base is set up, with its observatory, its garden, its power plant, and its radar station, it can go to work paying for itself. It will be a good place from which to observe the stars, better than Project X, which moves so fast that observations are difficult. But observations of the stars don't pay for anything.

The moon will not be of much use as a space-port, either. It is true that we need a speed of only two miles a second to get away from it, but the station in space gives us a better running start. The moon would be a good place for scientific research on how things behave in a vacuum, but the station would be just as good. No, if the moon base is going to pay for itself, it will have to be in some other way.

There is a chance that the other way could be found. On earth, the minerals we can use are not scattered evenly everywhere, but are found in small pockets of ore. More than likely, this is also true of the moon. The total weight of the moon is so small that there doesn't seem much chance of finding valuable heavy metals there. But there might be quantities of the very useful light metals like beryllium and aluminum.

Using the power of the sun engine, the moon base might soon be making its own metals and even exporting quantities of them back to the space station. It would cost less to send them from the moon than to bring them up from earth.

With these metals new space ships could be built at the station. And it might be possible to send some of the metals down to the earth.

But before we can think of transporting the moon metals, they must first be sought for and found. How are the explorers to travel as they look for metals on the moon?

Most of the vehicles we have on earth would not work there. No airplane can fly on the moon because of the lack of air, and our automobiles would be of no use, either. An electric automobile would work, but it would have to be re-designed for moon use. It could use only dry batteries, and because of the roughness of the moon's surface it would have to be more like a tank than an automobile. Even then it would be expensive to operate. Most of the exploring would still have to be done on foot, with the searching parties carrying their equipment in some kind of cart.

This is not quite as bad as it sounds. At one-sixth of the earth's gravity, walking around would be fairly easy, even in a space suit, and not as tiring as on earth. The only trouble would be getting up the sides of some of the big moon craters. The walls of some of them are higher than the highest mountains on earth. The job of exploring the whole moon will take a long time.

Another Use for the Moon Base

The moon observatory will be useful only for scientific purposes, but some of these might turn out to be very important. The moon's motion around the earth is quite slow, so a telescope placed there would be steadier than any in the observatories we now have. In addition, scientists could see better than they have ever seen from an earthly observatory because there are no clouds or air to blur the view. And the moon's light gravity is a help; it would enable us to make the supporting parts under the telescopes lighter than those on earth.

We shall learn a great deal more about our own solar system and the universe from this observatory. Possibly we shall learn enough about Mars to enable us to build just the right kind of space ship for going there. We may learn something about the mysterious planet of Venus, always hidden by its clouds.

Certainly we shall learn much more about the stars, and we are sure to discover more stars that, like our own sun, have planets of their own. A few of these have already been found, but the knowledge we have of them is only interesting; it is of no special use.

Battery-powered, tractor-mounted drill at work. Gravity one-sixth that of earth makes handling of heavy equipment easy.

Out there from the moon base, scientists may be able to find stars with planets like the earth. And if they are found, there may be men on them.

But the chances of reaching those yet undiscovered planets are not in sight. Even if we find the much improved fuels we need for setting up the space station and going to the moon, there is still not much chance of reaching the stars. It has been calculated that it would take a space ship three or four hundred years to reach the nearest star.

So we give up the idea of voyaging to other stars for a while. Let us think first about your trip to the moon. Later we can take up the problem of trying for Mars or Venus!